Shark Tooth Beach

Chase, Caitlyn, and Cooper,

Happy Reading!

Watch where you swim!

Gwen

Palmetto Publishing Group
Charleston, SC

Shark Tooth Beach
Copyright © 2019 by Gwen Ludvigsen
All rights reserved

First Edition

Printed in the United States

ISBN-13: 978-1-64111-311-3
ISBN-10: 1-64111-311-1
eBook ISBN: 978-1-64111-386-1

Shark Tooth Beach

by Gwen Ludvigsen

Did you know that sharks have been swimming in our oceans for millions of years? A long time ago, sharks were bigger than the sharks that live today. To find out about sharks, scientists need to study their teeth—only their teeth become fossilized.

Fossilized Sharks Teeth

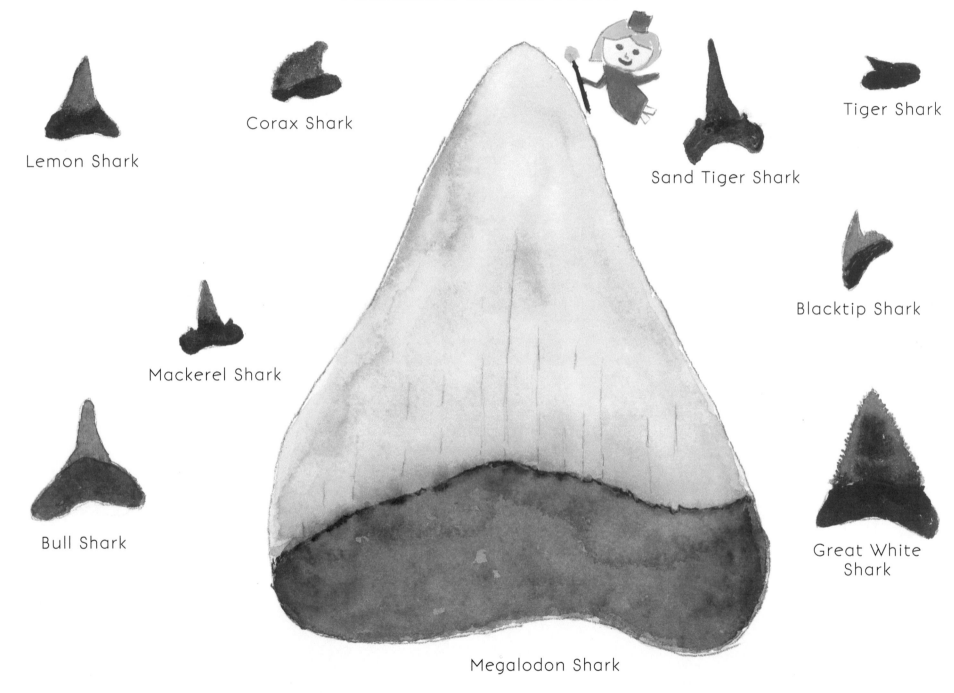

Corax Shark

Lemon Shark

Tiger Shark

Sand Tiger Shark

Blacktip Shark

Mackerel Shark

Bull Shark

Great White Shark

Megalodon Shark

A fossil is part of a plant or animal from a long time ago, like a dinosaur bone. Thankfully, there are plenty of sharks' teeth to be found. A shark loses and regrows new teeth. Scientists estimate they lose thirty thousand teeth in a lifetime. Wow! That's a big job for the shark tooth fairy!

The largest sharks that swam in our oceans were called megalodon sharks. These sharks, like the dinosaurs, are extinct. There are no megalodon sharks living today. From finding their teeth, we know they grew to be sixty feet long. Amazingly, that is as long as three great white sharks!

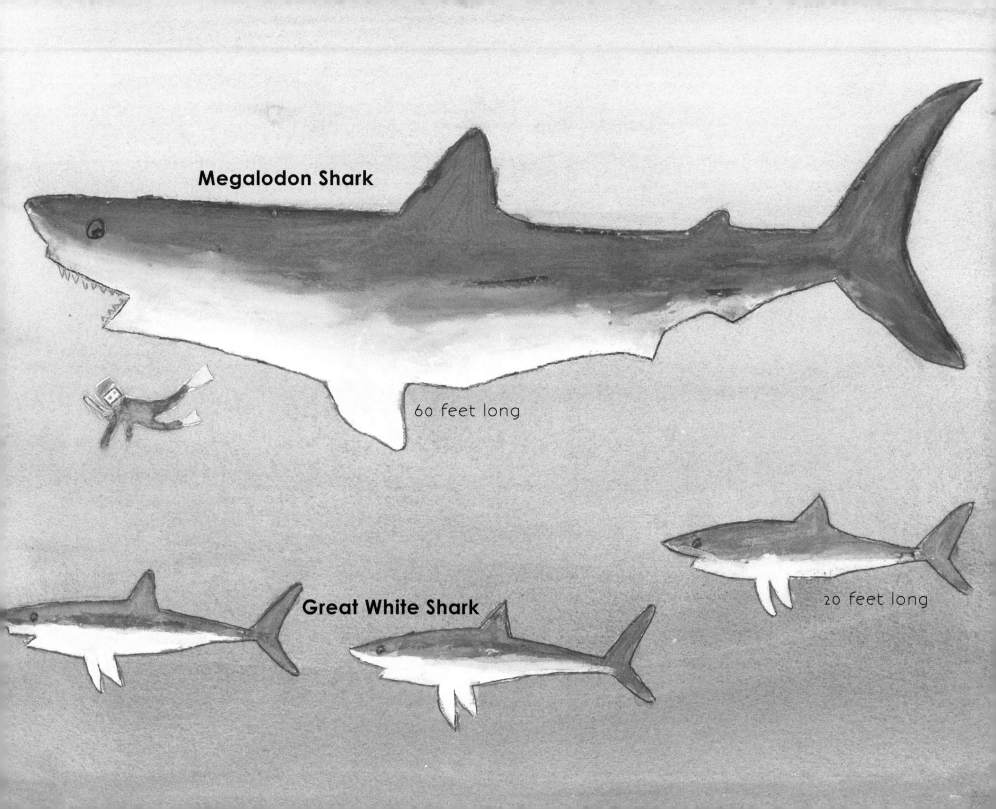

Megalodon Shark

60 feet long

Great White Shark

20 feet long

Sage closed her book, put it into her backpack, and ran to catch up with Mom and Dad. She and her family were on vacation. Each summer, they decided on an adventure. This summer, they were going to hunt for sharks' teeth on Shark Tooth Beach.

Sage and her family walked along the winding path that led to the beach. Finally, they could *see* the ocean.

"Yippee!" shouted Sage as she ran ahead and started digging in the sand. Visions of sharks' teeth danced in her head! Would they get lucky and find a megalodon tooth?

There was another family on the beach. A boy ran over to Sage. "Look," he said, "I found a shark's tooth." He held out his hand, and Sage saw a tiny black tooth. It was much smaller than she thought it would be.

"Thank you," said Sage, and they began digging together. Her new friend introduced himself as William. "I'm Sage," she said.

William's parents walked over to Sage's mom and dad. After a brief introduction, they were all hunting for sharks' teeth together.

"I found one!" shouted Sage's mom as she held up her treasure.

Before long, they each found a shark's tooth. The teeth were all different shapes and sizes. A shark needs many different types of teeth to hunt in the ocean.

It was almost time to leave the beach. Sage couldn't help but feel a little disappointed that she had not found a megalodon tooth. As she was packing up her things, her foot bumped into something buried in the sand. She brushed some of the sand away with her shovel. Everyone moved closer.

Her dad said, "I think it's a big tooth!" He reached down and gave it a great big tug. It was a huge tooth! From the size of it, they knew it was a megalodon tooth. Dad handed it to Sage.

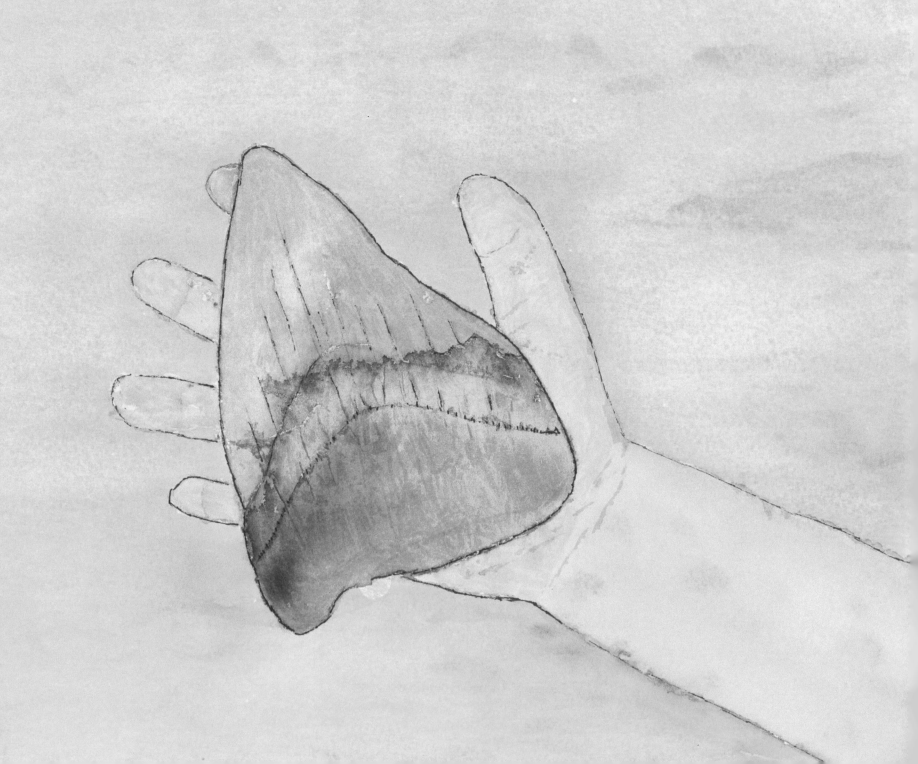

The tooth was almost as big as her hand. She was amazed to think that this tooth belonged to a shark that was swimming in the oceans millions of years ago.

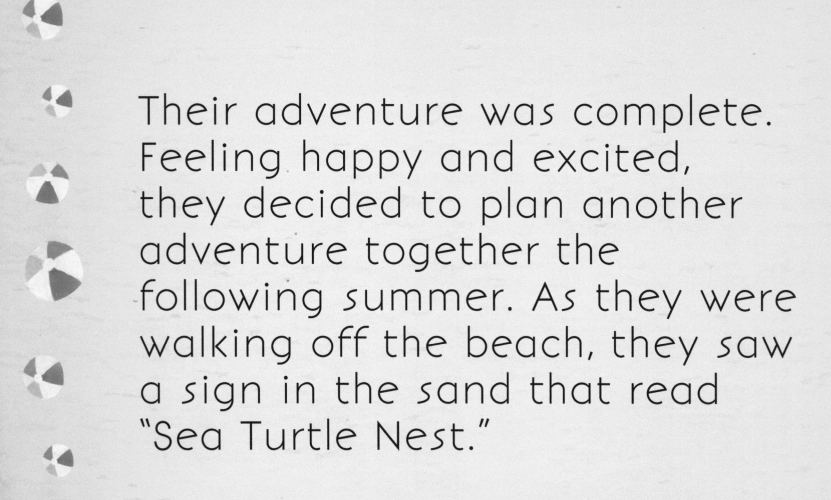

Their adventure was complete. Feeling happy and excited, they decided to plan another adventure together the following summer. As they were walking off the beach, they saw a sign in the sand that read "Sea Turtle Nest."

"Let's adopt a *sea* turtle nest and learn about loggerhead turtles on our next vacation," *suggested* Sage as they continued walking off the beach.

CPSIA information can be obtained
at www.ICGtesting.com
Printed in the USA
BVHW092033110619
550759BV00001BA/5/P